# ESSENTIAL PIANO SON
## TRANSCRIBED FOR Piano, Vocal & Gu

## WISE PUBLICATIONS
part of The Music Sales Group

London/New York/Paris/Sydney/Copenhagen/Berlin/Madrid/Tokyo

Published by
Wise Publications,
8/9 Frith Street, London, W1D 3JB, England.

Exclusive distributors:
Music Sales Limited,
Distribution Centre, Newmarket Road, Bury St Edmunds,
Suffolk, IP33 3YB, England.

Music Sales Pty Limited,
120 Rothschild Avenue, Rosebery,
NSW 2018, Australia.

Order No. AM91977
ISBN 0-7119-4093-2
This book © Copyright 2005 by Wise Publications.

Compiled by Nick Crispin.
Arranged by Mark Dickman, Paul Honey, Christopher Hussey,
Malcolm Miles & Quentin Thomas.
Engraved by Camden Music & Paul Ewers Music Design.

Printed in the United Kingdom.

www.musicsales.com

Your Guarantee of Quality:
As publishers, we strive to produce every book
to the highest commercial standards.

The music has been freshly engraved and the book has been
carefully designed to minimise awkward page turns and to make
playing from it a real pleasure. Particular care has been given
to specifying acid-free, neutral-sized paper made from pulps
which have not been elemental chlorine bleached.

This pulp is from farmed sustainable forests
and was produced with special regard for the environment.

Throughout, the printing and binding have been planned to ensure a sturdy,
attractive publication which should give years of enjoyment.

If your copy fails to meet our high standards, please inform us
and we will gladly replace it.

# Born To Lose

### Words & Music by Ted Daffan

3

# Drown In My Own Tears

### Words & Music by Henry Glover

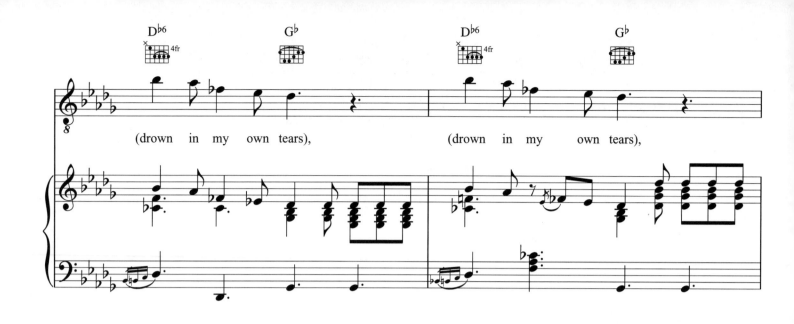

(drown in my own tears), (drown in my own tears),

(drown in my own tears), (drown in my own tears). I guess I'll

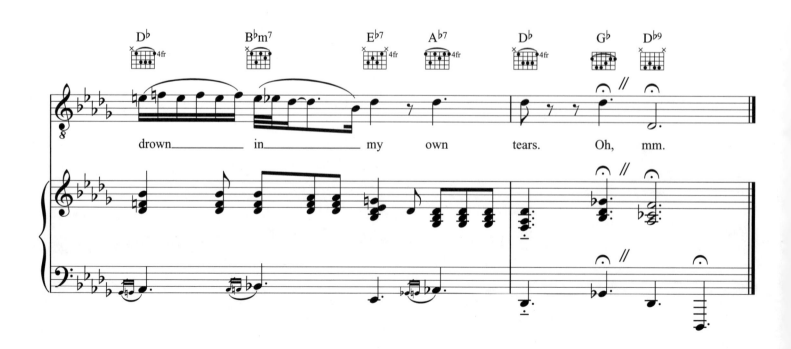

drown_____ in_____ my own tears. Oh, mm.

# Georgia On My Mind

**Words by Stuart Gorrell**
**Music by Hoagy Carmichael**

# Hallelujah I Love Her So

Words & Music by Ray Charles

Let me tell you 'bout a girl I know,— she is my ba-by and she

# Hard Times
# (No One Knows Better Than I)

Words & Music by Ray Charles

those hard___ times. Whoah, yeah._____ Who knows___ bet-ter than I?"___

Well I soon found___ out

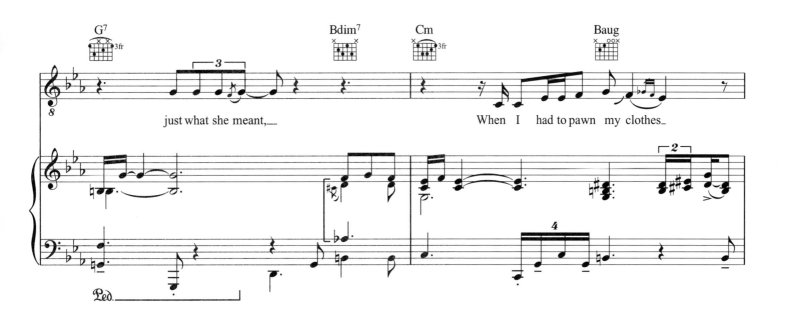

just what she meant,___ When I had to pawn my clothes___

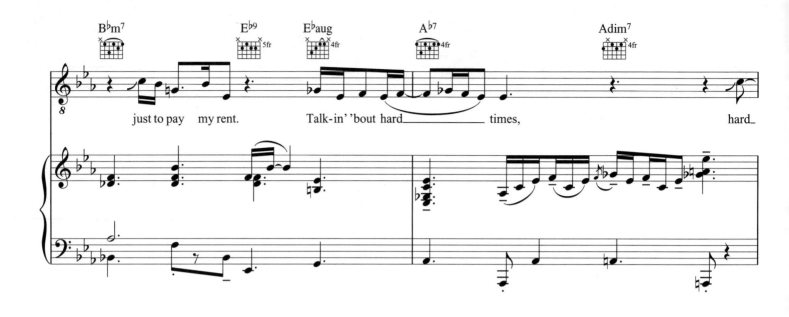

just to pay my rent. Talk-in' 'bout hard_____ times,      hard_

_ times._____ Whoah, yeah._____ Who knows      a -well a bet-ter than I?_

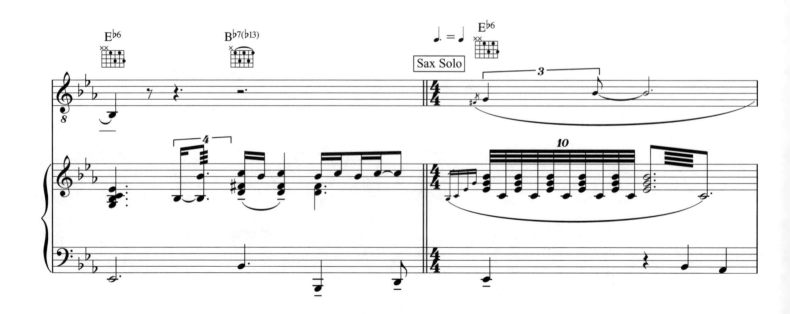

# Hit The Road Jack

### Words & Music by Percy Mayfield

Woah, wo-man, oh wo-man, don't treat me so____ mean; you're the mean-est old wo-man that I've ev-er seen.____ I guess if____ you said so,_____ I'll have to pack my things____ and____ go. (That's right! Hit the road,____ Jack and don't you come____ back no more, no more, no more, no more. Hit the

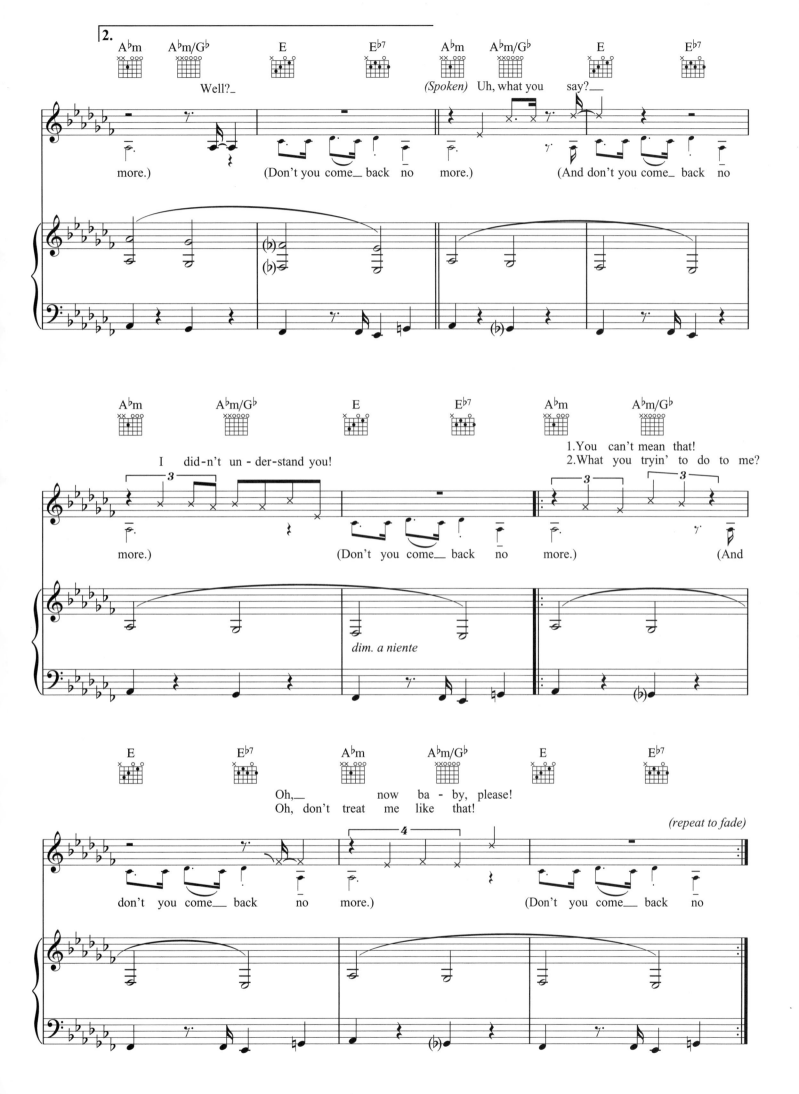

# I Believe To My Soul

### Words & Music by Ray Charles

# I Can't Stop Loving You

## Words & Music by Don Gibson

**Easy Swing** ♩=79

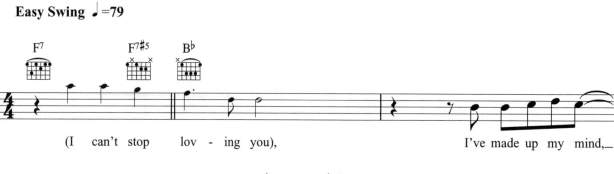

(I can't stop lov-ing you),      I've made up my mind,___

_____ to live in me - mo-ries___     of the lone - some

time.       (I can't stop want - ing you).

# Unchain My Heart

### Words & Music by Bobby Sharp & Teddy Powell

Original key A♭ minor

Un - chain my heart,___ ba - by let me be.___

Un - chain my heart,___ 'cos you don't care a-bout me.

# You Don't Know Me

### Words & Music by Cindy Walker & Eddy Arnold

a chance that you might love me too. You
give your hand___ to me,___ and then you say, "Good - bye". I watch you
walk a - way,___ be - side the luck - y guy.___ Oh, to nev - er,___
nev - er know___ the one___ who loves you so.___ Well,

you don't know___ me.

A - fraid and___ shy,_____ I let my chance go by,

a chance that you might love me too. Oh, you give your

# What'd I Say

## Words & Music by Ray Charles

♩=179

1. Hey ma-ma don't you treat me___wrong,     come and love your dad-dy all night long, al - right___
2. See the girl___ with the dia-mond ring,___     she knows how to    shake that thing, al - right___

___ now,          hey,___ hey,                    al -
___ now,          hey,___ hey,                    hey_____

-right.

**1.**

**2.**

Tell your ma-ma,      tell your pa,      I'm gon-na send you back to

64

al - right,

al - right.

Tell me what'd I say,____ tell me what'd I say,____
And____ I wanna know,____ said____ I wanna know,__

____ yeah.     And____ I wan-na know,
____ yeah.

Er,_____    oh,_____

Er,     oh,     er,     oh,     Woah,     one more     time.
Oh make me feel so     good,     Oh     it's     al - right,

Said a - one more time,___ ba - by now,
Make me feel so good___ now,_ yeah.
said that it's al - right___ right_ now,

said a - one more time_____ now,___    said a - one more    time,_
Woah,_____ Ba - by,_____    make me feel so    good_
said_ it's al - right,_____    said_ it's al - right_

___ yeah.    Said a - one more    time,___
___ yeah.    Make me feel so    good,___
___ yeah.    Said_ it's al - right,___

# Mess Around

## Words & Music by Ahmet Ertegun

Ah,___ you can

talk a - bout the pit, bar - be - cue, the band was jum - pin',

the peo - ple too. Ah, mess a - round, they do - in' the

mess a - round, they do - in' the mess a - round,

(Spoken) Now you got it boy...

Sax Solo

Yeah,

ah, mess around...